How to use this book

Follow the advice, in italics, given for you on each page.
Support the children as they read the text that is shaded in cream.
Praise *the children at every step!*

Detailed guidance is provided in the Read Write Inc. Phonics Handbook

9 reading activities

Children:
Practise reading the speed sounds.
Read the green, red and challenge words for the story.
Listen as you read the introduction.
Discuss the vocabulary check with you.
Read the story.
Re-read the story and discuss the 'questions to talk about'.
Read the story with fluency and expression.
Answer the questions to 'read and answer'.
Practise reading the speed words.

Speed sounds

Consonants *Say the pure sounds (do not add 'uh').*

f ff	l ll le	m mm	n nn (kn)	r rr	s ss	v ve	z zz	sh	th	ng nk

b bb	c k ck	d dd	g gg	h	j (ge)	p pp	qu	t tt	w wh	x	y	ch (tch)

Vowels *Say the sounds in and out of order.*

at	hen head	in	on	up	day	see happy he	high find	blow no

zoo	look	car	for door snore	fair	whirl	shout	boy spoil

*Each box contains one sound but sometimes more than one grapheme. Focus graphemes are **circled**.*

Green words

ch<u>ee</u>se   t<u>oo</u>   s<u>oo</u>n   <u>n</u>ight   ma<u>tch</u>   f<u>oo</u>d   hold   cold

<u>ar</u>m   j<u>ar</u>   <u>sh</u><u>ar</u>p   sm<u>ar</u>t   st<u>ar</u>   st<u>ar</u>t   p<u>ar</u>t   sc<u>ar</u>   c<u>ar</u>

M<u>ar</u>k   m<u>arge</u>   l<u>arge</u>   <u>ch</u><u>arge</u>   <u>gu</u><u>ar</u>d

---

Read in syllables.

ki<u>tch</u>`en  →  ki<u>tch</u>en     in`deed → indeed

hol`i`d<u>ay</u> → holid<u>ay</u>   c<u>ar</u>`toon → c<u>ar</u>toon

c<u>ar</u>`ton  →  c<u>ar</u>ton     B<u>ar</u>`ker → B<u>ar</u>ker

a`p<u>ar</u>t  →  ap<u>ar</u>t     F<u>ar</u>n`ham → F<u>ar</u>nham

C<u>ar</u>`di<u>ff</u>  →  C<u>ar</u>di<u>ff</u>     post`man → postman

Read the root word first and then with the ending.

bri<u>ng</u> → bri<u>ng</u>i<u>ng</u>   b<u>ar</u>ked → b<u>ar</u>ks· → b<u>ar</u>ki<u>ng</u>

begin → begi<u>nn</u>i<u>ng</u>   st<u>ar</u>t → st<u>ar</u>ted → st<u>ar</u>ti<u>ng</u>

<u>kn</u>o<u>ck</u> → <u>kn</u>o<u>ck</u>ed

Red words

does   w<u>e</u>re   a<u>ll</u>   <u>o</u>ne   s<u>ai</u>d

Challenge words

gr<u>ey</u>   p<u>aw</u>   wa<u>sh</u>ed

Barker

Introduction

Do you have a dog?
Imagine owning a really naughty dog. Barker is a big,
dark grey dog that is always barking. He gets into lots
of trouble for doing bad things and he is always being
told off. Then one night he barks at the right time.

What do you think he does?

Story written by Gill Munton
Illustrated by Tim Archbold

Vocabulary check

Discuss the meaning (as used in the story) after the children have read each word.

	definition:	sentence/phrase:
fed up	cross with	They were all fed up with Barker.
darts match	throwing game	Grandad was at a darts match.
pinch	take	Then he started to pinch food.
chunk	bit	He was running away with a big chunk of beef.
keen	pleased or liked	Mum wasn't too keen on muddy paw marks.
charged	rushed	Barker charged up to him.
guard dog	a dog that protects people	Meet Barker the guard dog!

Punctuation to note in this story:
1. Capital letters to start sentences and full stops to end sentences
2. Capital letters for names
3. Exclamation marks to show anger, shock and surprise
4. 'Wait and see' dots...
5. Apostrophe to show contractions: wasn't you're

Barker

Barker's my dog.

He's the best!

He's big, dark grey and a bit smelly.

(He rolls in mud a lot.)

He barks a lot, too. In fact, he does lots of bad things.

Mum, Dad, Grandad and the postman were all fed up with Barker.

Until the day that ...

No, let's start at the beginning with Grandad's slippers.

Barker had lots of fun with them. One night,
when Grandad was at a darts match, Barker
got hold of one of the slippers
and ripped it apart!

Grandad said, "No, Barker."
And Barker just barked.

Then he started to pinch food from the kitchen. Jam tarts, cheese sandwiches and jelly. Barker wasn't fussy.

Mum left a dish of cold beef on a shelf, and Barker jumped up to get it. A carton of milk, a jar of plum jam – Barker knocked them off the shelf to get to the beef.

He looked like a cartoon dog, running away from Mum with a big chunk of beef between his teeth!

Mum said, "No, Barker."
And Barker just barked.

Oh, yes, and Mum wasn't too keen on the muddy paw marks.
When Barker slept on my bed one night, the sheets had to be
washed the next day!

I said, "No, Barker."

And Barker just barked.

The best part was when Barker bit the postman. He was bringing us a postcard from Dad's pal Mark (on holiday in Cardiff).

Barker charged up to him and bit his arm!
(He's got sharp teeth, my dog.
The postman's still got the scar!)

The postman said, "No, Barker."
And Barker just barked.

Barker's best trick was being sick in the car. One day, we went shopping in Farnham. Barker grabbed an old hotdog from a bin, and when we got back to the car he looked a bit ill.

We all got in, and as soon as Dad started

up the car, Barker was sick ...

very sick indeed.

And we were still in the car park!

Dad said "No Barker."

And Barker just barked.

Then, one night, he started
barking when we were all asleep in bed!

Dad went to see what was up.
The kitchen window was smashed, and
Dad spotted some men running away
from the flat!

"Meet Barker the guard dog!" I said.

"Smart dog, Barker! You're a star!"

That night, they all agreed with me.

Questions to talk about

Re-read the page. Read the question to the children. Tell them whether it is a **FIND IT** question or **PROVE IT** question.

FIND IT

✔ Turn to the page

✔ Read the question

✔ Find the answer

PROVE IT

✔ Turn to the page

✔ Read the question

✔ Find your evidence

✔ Explain why

Page 9:	FIND IT	How would you describe Barker?
Page 10:	FIND IT	What did Barker do to Grandad's slipper?
Page 11:	PROVE IT	Why was Mum cross with Barker?
Page 12:	FIND IT	What did Barker do to the bed?
Page 13:	PROVE IT	Why do you think Barker bit the postman?
Page 14:	PROVE IT	What made Barker sick?
Page 15:	PROVE IT	Why did everyone think Barker was a star at the end?

Questions to read and answer

(Children complete without your help.)

1. What did Barker do with Grandad's slipper?
   He ripped it apart. / He hid it. / He licked it.

2. What did Barker pinch from the kitchen?
   **He pinched drinks from the kitchen. /He pinched food from the kitchen. /
   He pinched slippers from the kitchen.**

3. What did Barker do to the postman?
   Barker licked the postman. / Barker bit the postman.

4. What did Barker do in the car?
   Barker slept in the car. / Barker hid in the car. / Barker was sick in the car.

5. What did Dad say to Barker in the end?
   You are a sad dog. / You are a smart dog. / You are a bad dog.

Speed words

Children practise reading the words across the rows, down the columns and in and out of order clearly and quickly.

bringing	beginning	soon	too	looked
indeed	sharp	barked	part	car
started	jar	all	one	wasn't
does	he's	you're	hold	cold